TIBETANS

Judith Kendra

WAYLAND

First published in 1993 by Wayland

Copyright © Wayland 1993
Revised and updated 2008

Wayland
338 Euston Road
London NW1 3BH

Wayland Australia
Level 17/207 Kent Street
Sydney NSW 2000

Series editor: Paul Mason
Designer: Kudos Editorial and Design Services

This edition
Wayland Commissioning Editor: Jennifer Sanderson
Design: Robert Walster
Editor: Sonya Newland

Acknowledgements
The artwork on page 18 was supplied by Peter Bull.
The publishers gratefully acknowledge the permission of
the following to use their pictures: Corbis 29 and cover
(Alison Wright); Eye Ubiquitous 17, 20, 32, 45; Jim
Holmes/Himalayan Images 4, 5, 11, 12 right, 14, 19, 21,
36, 39, 40, 44; Royal Geographical Society 16; Tibet
Image Bank 6 (Robin Bath), 7 (P Collinson), 8 (J Miles),
9 (SJ&BB), 12 left (R Bath), 13 (H Richardson), 15
(Stone Routes), 22 (1 Kristalis), 23 (left V Sis & J Vanis,
right Stone Routes), 24 (S Jones), 25, 26 (both
R Schwarz), 27 (I Kristalis), 28, 30, 31 (all Tibet
Information Network), 33, 34, 35 (all Stone Routes),
37 (C Langdon), 38 (J Andersson), 41 (C Langdon),
42, 43 (Tibet Image Bank).

A CIP catalogue record for this book is available from
the British Library.

ISBN 978 0 7502 5576 9

Printed in Singapore

Wayland is a division of Hachette Children's Books,
an Hachette Livre UK company.
www.hachettelivre.co.uk

This book has been produced in consultation with
the Minority Rights Group; an international non-
governmental organization working to secure justice
for ethnic, linguistic, religious and social minorities
worldwide who are suffering discrimination.

Contents

1 Introduction

For centuries, people have talked and wondered about Tibet, but they have rarely been able to penetrate its borders. Even if they could overcome the physical obstacles, they were not generally allowed inside. The more secret it seemed, the more people wanted to go there – but very few were successful. The rest had to be content to listen to stories of a spectacularly beautiful land, hidden behind a curtain of mountains. These stories intrigued travellers so much they called it Shangri-La ('earthly paradise').

⬅ Three monks talking at Tashilumpo Monastery in Tibet. Most Tibetans follow the Buddhist religion.

⊕ Mount Kailash is Tibet's holiest mountain. Pilgrims travel many kilometres to visit the mountain.

The roof of the world

About 40 million years ago, huge pressures on the Earth's surface pushed up a great plateau about 4,000 metres above sea level. This plateau is now called Tibet. The same pressures formed some of the world's highest mountains and crowded them all round the edge of the plateau. It was almost completely surrounded by mountains, except in the north-east. This meant that any travellers had to climb very high indeed to reach the borders of Tibet.

Once inside, they found a country almost the size of western Europe. In the north (the Changtang) were wide-open plains and salt flats, dotted here and there by lakes with crystallized salt sparkling on their shores. In the south, in the province of U-Tsang, were greener valleys, sheltered by the high Himalayan mountains. Here, farmers grew barley, fruit and vegetables, and several

towns were situated near the Tsangpo River, including the capital of Tibet, Lhasa. In the east, in the Kham province, the valleys were heavily forested with dramatic gorges and rivers rushing through the trees. Many wild animals lived in this area. Tibet's third province, Amdo, lay in the north-east and had an incredible mixture of plains, forests, mountains and rivers. From some places it was possible to see a great distance across to snow-capped mountains.

Far from Western influence

Colonel Francis Younghusband, a British army officer, visited Tibet in 1904. He and his men reported that the Tibetans were a peaceful people who followed the Buddhist religion and were ruled by a god-king called the Dalai Lama. The country seemed incredibly old-fashioned. There were no roads. The Tibetans had few Western

Beautiful statues of the Buddha were once found in monasteries all over Tibet. Sometimes pictures of the Dalai Lama were propped up in front.

possessions: they had their own way of life, and it seemed colourful and fascinating.

Later, in the middle of the Second World War (1939–45), an Austrian called Heinrich Harrer escaped from a prisoner-of-war camp in India. He and a friend managed to walk all the way to Tibet. They slipped across the border – something no uninvited foreigner was allowed to do. When they eventually reached Lhasa, the Tibetan officials were so astonished to see Harrer and his friend that they were allowed to stay. Harrer lived there for seven years and got to know the Dalai Lama, who was a boy of only eight when Harrer arrived. He had been Dalai Lama for three years. Then, in 1950, the Chinese invaded and Harrer had to leave.

Chinese invasion

The Chinese government invaded Tibet for a number of reasons. Firstly, they wanted to make it difficult for anyone to attack China from the west. Secondly, they wanted Tibet's wealth: statues made of gold, silver and precious stones that were kept in the monasteries, trees that could be cut down as timber and minerals found under the ground. Thirdly, for a long time the Chinese had claimed that Tibet was a part of the Chinese Empire, even though most Tibetans and historians dispute this.

So, in 1950, the Chinese authorities sent an army marching towards the gap in the mountains. Tibetan resistance was very confused and the soldiers were poorly equipped. The Tibet government had never thought it important to make friends with the rest of the world. So when it asked other countries to help, none of them would do anything in case they angered the Chinese, who were much more powerful. Tibet was overrun very easily.

Life in occupied Tibet

Occupation has been a disaster for Tibet. In an effort to keep control of the country over the past 60 years, the Chinese have killed, imprisoned and tortured thousands of Tibetans. They have meted out such harsh punishments for the smallest so-called crimes (such as owning a picture of the Dalai Lama) that even other countries have complained strongly to the Chinese about it.

At the same time, the Chinese authorities have completely reorganized the way of life in the country so that the Tibetans can no longer live as they would like to do, practise their religion as they want, nor prevent their precious and beautiful environment from being destroyed.

This story is not yet finished. Today, the Tibetan people are struggling to keep their way of life and their country. They are struggling for survival.

⬆ Chinese guards and Tibetan monks all gather in the capital Lhasa. The Chinese presence is evident all over the country.

2 Family life

Lifestyles in Tibet depend on which part of the country people live in. Those in Lhasa, if they are employed, work either in 'official' Chinese jobs that allow them certain privileges, or in work not attached to the state, in which case they do not have access to such benefits. Those who live in the fertile river valleys are able to farm the land and to rear animals on it because the soil is good and the weather is right. For people who live in the Changtang, the open plains of Tibet, this lifestyle is not possible.

Although the latitude there is the same as that of the Canary Islands or Houston, the high altitude of the Changtang makes the weather closer to that of Alaska. Midday temperatures in the winter might be just above freezing but at night they can drop to -35°C. The only agriculture possible on this kind of terrain is raising sheep, goats and yaks, and this is what the nomads on the Changtang do. The people adapt their way of life to the harsh environment, even if this means constantly moving their flocks and having very few possessions, so that they can be as mobile as possible.

Life on the Changtang

Growing up on the Changtang is a totally different experience to growing up in Lhasa. Pema Norbu is the 12-year-old daughter of a family of nomads. She and her family live in a tent made from yaks' hair on the open grassland. In the spring, summer and winter they stay in the same place near a turquoise lake, but in the autumn they move the tent

Tea and tsampa

Tibetans make their tea in a different way to Westerners. The leaves are first boiled in a pot of water and then mixed with salt and a lump of butter, and poured into a long wooden churn. By pumping a plunger up and down inside the churn, it is thoroughly mixed together and then served in a small clay or metal bowl.

The most popular food of the Tibetans is tsampa. This is cooked barley that has been ground to the consistency of flour. Needing almost no preparation, tsampa can be eaten dry, or mixed with tea, butter, dried cheese or yoghurt.

🔽 A woman wearing Tibetan national dress, pouring tea from a wooden churn.

⬆ Nomads rear their livestock on the grasslands, which make up 70 per cent of Tibet.

about two days' walk away so that the animals can find fresh grass to eat.

One of Pema's tasks is to look after the sheep and goats while they are grazing. Her father tells her where to take them, and in the morning she puts on her heavy coat made from 10 sheep skins, her hat and long, coloured boots, and goes off with the animals. She is out there all alone until evening and is supposed to make sure the sheep and goats stay together and that wolves do not come too close. Pema was only eight when her father first asked her to do the work. She was pleased then because it

made her feel grown up. Now, after four years, the days seem to pass slowly sometimes, but since there is no school in the area she might just as well be out with the animals.

Life in Lhasa

Paljor Sonam is the same age as Pema but his life in Lhasa is totally different. He and his family live in a traditional Tibetan house, with large windows and thick mud walls. They have trouble making ends meet, because Paljor's father is unemployed. Luckily one of his uncles has a good job as a truck driver and gives them extra money when he can. Another uncle is a monk: he was imprisoned after the big demonstration against the Chinese in 1989. No one knows where he is, or if he is still alive.

When Paljor is not at school, he sometimes sits with his father in the main square near the Jokhang, Lhasa's biggest cathedral, and watches people go by. Even though his truck-driver uncle says not all the Chinese are bad, Paljor still doesn't like to get too close to the Chinese soldiers. He doesn't like to get too close to the Tibetan *Khampas* either, but for a different reason. They have a reputation as fearless fighters (he had heard they fought bravely against the Chinese when they invaded Tibet) and

they always look so proud as they stride round the square. He wishes he could wear clothes like them and not the green Chinese cap and trousers that he and all his friends have to wear.

Paljor has just started secondary school, which means he now has to learn his lessons in Chinese rather than Tibetan. As if that's not enough, the Chinese boys his age have started calling him names, such as 'crazy barbarian'. Paljor would rather spend his free time with his friends playing at *Khampa* warriors down by the stream. The best time of day for this is when the sun dips low behind the Potala, the palace of the Dalai Lama before he was forced to flee Tibet after the Chinese invasion.

◉ A *Khampa* warrior. The *Khampas* are famous for their bright clothes and they often wear beads in their hair.

3 Country and culture

The Potala

There are over 1,000 rooms, assembly halls and chapels inside the Potala (in the background above). The two outside sections, painted white, once housed the Dalai Lama's private monastery, a school for monk officials, various government offices and the meeting halls of the National Assembly. The central part, coloured dark red on the outside, was the religious palace and still contains the tombs of nine previous Dalai Lamas. These are incredible pointed structures, covered with gold leaf and sparkling jewels, which are found deep in the heart of the building. Around them in the dim shrine rooms flicker hundreds of small lamps, whose tiny lights make the gold of the tombs and the Buddha statues glow. Before the Chinese came, the store-rooms below were filled with treasures and precious religious books. No one knows what has become of these.

The Potala, the Dalai Lama's palace (in the background in the picture above), stands on a high hill and dominates the city of Lhasa. Rebuilt in the seventeenth century, it is 13 storeys high and took 40 years to complete. Not far away, in the heart of the city, is the seventh-century Jokhang, Tibet's main cathedral, which contains one of the two oldest and most revered statues in Tibet. These buildings are the heart of Tibetan life.

The present Dalai Lama no longer lives in Tibet, but before he fled from the Chinese in 1950 he spent a great deal of time inside the Potala. He was head of both religious and political life in Tibet and it was inside this

⬆ The yak is related to the ox and can be as much as two metres tall at the shoulder.

Self-sufficiency

Tibet was self-sufficient in food: barley was the staple crop and famine was unknown. Every autumn, when the harvest was gathered, traders formed large mule, yak and camel trains and journeyed north to Mongolia, east to China and south to India. There they traded such goods as salt, gold dust, wool, herbs and yak tails for tea, tobacco, horses, Chinese silks, silver and matches. The yak tails were used in other countries as fly whisks and false beards.

Prayer wheels

Hand-held prayer wheels consist of a small rod with a revolving circular compartment on top. After they have been blessed by a monk, this top section is filled with pieces of paper that have prayers written on them. As an act of devotion, a pilgrim might walk clockwise round the outside of a monastery, turning a prayer wheel in the same direction in his or her hand. Much larger, free-standing prayer wheels can be anything from about half a metre in height to those that fill an entire room.

building that most of the government and central religious affairs were carried out.

Beneath the Dalai Lama (and his deputy, the Panchen Lama) there was a hierarchy of monks and nobility who held power. Tibet was a society in which most land was owned either by aristocratic families or by the monasteries. Whoever owned an estate had the right to collect taxes from the ordinary people who lived within its boundaries. They were tied to their particular lord and were not allowed to move around the country without permission. Life could be hard for the peasants, but their masters did offer them a degree of protection. Women were considered equal in status to men, something unusual in the rest of Asia even today.

⬆ This picture shows Ganden monastery before the Chinese invasion. It was one of the largest and most famous monasteries in Tibet and once housed 6,000 monks.

Role of the monasteries

The Buddhist religion had been strong in Tibet for over 1,000 years when the Chinese army invaded. Many monasteries had been built throughout the country: by the time the Chinese soldiers invaded there were probably about 6,000 of them in the three provinces. Some were attached to small villages and some, especially Sera, Ganden and Drepung near Lhasa, were so big they were like small towns in themselves. The largest contained about 10,000 monks of all ages, some of them children. The children's parents sent them to the monastery for religious reasons or because education there was good.

It is likely that nearly one-sixth of all the men in the country were monks at any one time. (Women could be nuns, but there were not so many of them.) The monasteries were centres of learning and culture, where religious studies, art, architecture, medicine and literature were taught and researched. Some monks studied for 20 years before taking the highest exams. The monasteries were the places where priceless books and works of art had been kept for centuries.

Wheels and flags

Tibetans believe that turning prayer wheels, setting up prayer flags and prostrating are some of the many ways of becoming a better person in the future. Turning prayer wheels sends prayers out into the world. Prayer flags are pieces of coloured cloth with prayers printed on them: every time the wind flaps the flag prayers blow out into the air. Prayer flags are fixed to the roofs of houses, the tops of mountain passes or to bridges.

Prostrating is a special kind of gesture used to show respect and humility to a god. In Tibet, people like to prostrate either in front of a particular sacred statue or in a clockwise direction around certain places. The most important spot is inside the Jokhang, or central cathedral, of Lhasa. The second circular route is called the Barkhor and is a path that goes round the Jokhang on the outside. The third used to be the Lingkhor and was a six-kilometre-long road that encircled the city. These three routes were always crammed with pilgrims.

Festivals

Religious festivals were celebrated enthusiastically. The most important of all was the Monlam, or Great Prayer Festival, which was held at the Jokhang cathedral. Thousands of monks and ordinary people came to Lhasa for three weeks to take part in special religious services, public sermons, parades, horse races and other colourful

Prostration

The most devout pilgrims prostrate round a building or a statue. In earlier times, a few pilgrims from eastern Tibet might prostrate right across the country, from their homes to Lhasa – a journey that might take three years. They needed to wear special pads on their knees and hands, as well as a leather apron, to protect themselves.

The most elaborate form of prostration has four positions. First, place your palms together and raise them above your head, then bring them down (still together) and touch the tips of your index fingers to your forehead, next to your lips and lastly to your heart. After this, you can sink to your knees and, pushing your outstretched arms in front of you, place your face on the floor. Marking where your fingertips reach in the dust, you raise yourself to your feet and move to stand at the mark. Then you repeat the movement again.

events. The monks put on their best clothes: incredible yellow and red curved hats, special robes and silk scarves if they had them. New lamps were lit in front of jewel-encrusted images of the Buddha, enormous painted sculptures made out of butter were placed near the Jokhang, music was played and, throughout most of the proceedings, the Dalai Lama and other important monks sat and watched from a platform high up beside the cathedral.

'Attack from without and within'

Before the Chinese invasion, Tibetan civilization had existed for more than 1,000 years, and seemed unlikely to end.

⊕ Musician monks playing their instruments, dressed in their finest clothes to attend a festival.

Finding the Fourteenth Dalai Lama

Two years after the Thirteenth Dalai Lama died, Tibet's temporary ruler saw a vision in a lake that he believed would help him find the next Dalai Lama. In the clear waters, he could make out a white road leading east from a monastery with gold and jade rooftops. At the end of the road was a house with turquoise-coloured tiles and a brown and white spotted dog in the courtyard. Later, he dreamed of the same house and its oddly shaped gutters. Soon, members of a search party were sent out to Amdo province in the north-east, where they found the monastery of the vision. They investigated children in the area for six months before hearing about an intriguing little boy in the farming village of Taktser.

Disguising themselves as merchants, the senior monks and officials tracked down the village and, in it, found a modest house with turquoise tiles and the same twisted waterspouts of the dream. In the yard, a brown and white dog began to bark and, in the kitchen, they found a toddler aged two-and-a-half. They tested him by placing several objects on a table, some of which had been owned by the previous Dalai Lama, and the little boy unhesitatingly chose the right ones. Next, they examined his body for traditional markings and found three out of eight. There was no longer any doubt: they had found the Fourteenth Dalai Lama.

⬆ The Dalai Lama as a small boy. He was only five years old when he first became the ruler of Tibet.

However, in 1932, the Thirteenth Dalai Lama made a terrible prophecy: 'It may happen that here, in the centre of Tibet, religion and government will be attacked both from without and from within. Unless we can guard our own country, it will now happen that the Dalai and Panchen Lamas, the Father and the Son, and all the revered holders of the Faith, will disappear and become nameless. Monks and their monasteries will be destroyed. The rule of law will be weakened. The lands and property of government officials will be seized. They themselves will be forced to serve their enemies or wander the country like beggars. All beings will be sunk in great hardship and overpowering fear; the days and nights will drag on slowly in suffering.'

A year later, the Thirteenth Dalai Lama died. The search began for his successor. He might be anywhere in the country and would only be discovered by following certain omens, visions and signs that high-ranking monks and politicians might understand. It took four years to find a small boy called Lhamo Dhondrub and to be sure that he was the right person. In 1940 he was made Dalai Lama in the great Eastern Hall of the Potala. He was five years old. Ten years later the Chinese invaded his country.

4 The Chinese invasion

In 1950, the Chinese People's Liberation Army invaded Tibet. Over the next nine years the Chinese authorities gradually increased their control over the country by building roads, collecting taxes and forcibly changing the Tibetan way of life to be more in line with the Communist system.

By March 1959, conditions were so bad for the Tibetans in Lhasa that they rebelled against the Chinese. However, since they had virtually no modern weapons, they were powerless against the troops, who crushed the revolt (now called the National Uprising) and arrested and executed large numbers of Tibetans. It was at this time that the Dalai Lama fled to India, because he felt he could be more use to his people outside the country than inside it. One hundred thousand people followed him into exile.

Social changes

After the National Uprising, immense changes to Tibetan social and religious life were begun by the Chinese authorities.

⬆ Exiled Tibetans in Dharamsala, India, demonstrating against the occupation of their country, remembering the anniversary of the Tibetan Uprising in 1959.

The map above shows the extent of Tibet before the Chinese invasion.
Below you can see the size of China's Tibet Autonomous Region.

One of these was the renaming, in 1965, of U-Tsang Province as the Tibet Autonomous Region (TAR), which is all that the Chinese government now recognizes as Tibet. The other two provinces, Kham and Amdo, were no longer recognized by the Chinese, who said that they were part of China. This meant that it became impossible for the Tibetans to negotiate with the Chinese on behalf of all their people.

Liberation and modernization

The Chinese Army saw itself as 'liberating' (freeing) Tibetan peasants from their 'old-fashioned' past and as 'modernizing' the country for the benefit of all. But the Tibetans saw only that their country had been invaded using excessive violence, and that they were being forced to live as second-class citizens in their own land.

It is true that the Chinese have made improvements such as building roads, starting up industries, modernizing agriculture and building more hospitals and schools. However, as the years have gone by, it has become clear that these improvements actually benefit the Chinese and a few Tibetan officials far more than they help ordinary Tibetans. For example, the roads were built for military purposes and for logging, and the industries employ Chinese workers. Most people are now a great deal worse off than they were before the Chinese arrived.

The Cultural Revolution

Between 1966 and 1979 especially, officials of the Chinese Communist Party were determined to get rid of all 'old traditions, old thoughts, old culture and old customs'. This campaign to get rid of the 'four olds'

◐ Broken statues found at the Dalai Lama's summer palace. The precious contents of the monasteries and palaces were destroyed by Chinese soldiers.

↑ Ganden Monastery was destroyed by the Red Guards in 1967.

was part of a period of Chinese history called the Cultural Revolution. During this period, many thousands of people lost their lives and many precious things were destroyed in both China and Tibet.

Although the Cultural Revolution ended in 1976 in China, it was not until 1979 that the situation improved in Tibet. The Chinese realized they had made many catastrophic mistakes in the previous few years and the authorities made life easier for the Tibetans for a while. However, this period did not last long. From about 1987 onwards, life in the country, especially in Lhasa, grew more tense.

Destruction of the monasteries

Since the monasteries played such an important part in Tibetan life, the Chinese authorities believed that if they destroyed them they would have greater control over the country. By 1978, all but 13 of the nearly 6,000 monasteries and religious monuments in Tibet had been ruined. Almost all the works of art, books and other treasures inside them had been burned, sold or destroyed. For many years, the Jokhang in Lhasa was used as a pigsty and an army barracks. The Linkhor, one of the sacred paths used for prostrations, had roads and new buildings built across it so that it was no longer possible to use it properly.

Before the invasion there were more than 100,000 monks in the monasteries of Central Tibet, but by 1966 only 6,700 remained. The rest had been imprisoned, killed or sent home. Within just a few years, the link between the monasteries, the monks and the local communities was broken.

During the Cultural Revolution, Tibetans were not allowed to practise Buddhism.

From the late 1970s, however, the Chinese authorities began to allow some religious activities and, in the last few years, a few new monks have been ordained. However, they are carefully watched by the authorities.

Reconstruction and further decline

Some money was made available to rebuild a very small number of the monasteries on the tourist routes. The Jokhang was reopened and partially restored. In 1986, the Monlam Prayer Festival was celebrated for the first time in 20 years. However, since 1987, large numbers of monks and nuns have once again been imprisoned and tortured for playing a major part in demonstrations for independence.

By March 1989, relations between the authorities and the Tibetans were so strained that the Chinese brought in martial law (rule by the army). Soldiers and tanks were stationed on the streets of Lhasa and within 60 km of the city for just over a year, and tight control was kept on all Tibetans, especially those in the monasteries. In 1989, Tibetans refused to celebrate the Monlam Prayer Festival because they said the Chinese were using it to pretend the situation was calm when it was not. The following year, the Chinese government banned the Festival altogether.

⬇ In the mid-1980s, a few monasteries were rebuilt because the Chinese rulers are keen for tourists to visit Tibet.

Education

While the Chinese have built over 1,000 schools in Tibet in the last 60 years, it is they, rather than the Tibetans, who benefit from them the most. In many rural areas – where few Chinese live – there are no schools at all. At primary level, Tibetan children learn their lessons in their own language and, from the age of nine, receive three hours of Chinese language tuition a week. Chinese pupils are separated from the Tibetans and educated in Chinese. They spend three hours a week learning the Tibetan language.

Only five per cent of Tibetan children go on to secondary school at 12 years old. Of those who do, only one-third of them stay for the full six years because, at this level, lessons are taught in Chinese. They find it harder to understand their lessons and eventually many of them give up. Chinese children are learning in their own language and do far better at school. It is easy to see why some Chinese jeer at Tibetans and quite wrongly call them stupid. Ordinary Tibetan children are not allowed to learn English at secondary school. However, those who have not studied English are not allowed to take science subjects in any Chinese university.

Employment

The result of this school system is that a high percentage of Tibetans are illiterate.

⬆ At primary level, Tibetan children's lessons are in their own language. Because secondary lessons are taught in Chinese, the Tibetan's find them hard, and so few complete their secondary schooling.

⬆ Before the Chinese invasion of Tibet, Lhasa (left) was a relatively small town. Now, many new buildings have been built (above). Many of them out of keeping with the Tibetan style of architecture.

This makes it difficult for Tibetans to get jobs in the state system. If they manage to find unofficial work, they do not receive as much food or as many holidays and other privileges as someone working for the state. Basically, Tibetans do not receive enough education to be able to compete well enough with the Chinese for jobs and,

as a result, unemployment rates are high among native Tibetans.

The new settlers

Since the early 1980s, the Chinese authorities have encouraged Chinese people to live and work in Tibet. Around 60,000 workers were sent from China to help with

⬆ Chinese traders in a market in Tibet. The Chinese control much of the trade in Lhasa, and because they are paid more than the Tibetans, they can afford better food.

building programmes and other schemes to begin with, and there are now estimated to be 7.5 million Chinese in Tibet. Many of them complain about living there. They say it is remote, cold, lacking in comforts and peopled by barbarians. They are persuaded to stay by good wages and other benefits. A Chinese teacher, for example, can earn five times more in Tibet than he or she can at home. Other encouragements include a special altitude allowance (because of the height of the Tibetan plateau), a remoteness bonus, lower taxes, less hours of work and longer holidays.

Effects of immigration

In recent years, therefore, thousands of Chinese migrants have been persuaded to move to Tibet, attracted by these incentives. This new situation is worrying Tibetans, who fear that soon there will be more Chinese than Tibetans in their country. Already, it is believed that at least 7.5 million Chinese live alongside the six million Tibetans, but it is difficult to be sure of these figures because the Chinese government does not allow the outside world much information about the situation. Certainly, the population of Lhasa is already more than 50 per cent Chinese.

If Chinese settlers continue to pour into the country, Tibetans will hold less and less political power in their own country. Another consequence of so many new settlers is that the Tibetan culture is likely to be washed away by a rising flood of 'Chineseness'. There are already signs that this is happening.

5 Human rights

In 1948, the United Nations adopted the Universal Declaration of Human Rights. This laid down rights that everyone in the world should be able to have so that they can live a decent life. Having such rights as freedom from torture, freedom of thought and religion, the right to gather together in one place with other people, and the right to a fair trial were believed to be the 'foundation of freedom, justice and peace in the world'.

Measuring up

This Universal Declaration of Human Rights has become a way of testing how much a government cares for its people. If its actions do not measure up to the Declaration, that

⬆ Tibetans demonstrating in Lhasa on the fortieth anniversary of the Universal Declaration of Human Rights. During this demonstration, the monk leading the march was shot dead by the police.

⬆ Chinese troops massing in Lhasa before the demonstration held on 10 December 1988. It is estimated that there are 300,000 Chinese soldiers stationed in Tibet.

government may be criticized by such organizations as Amnesty International, which exists specifically to search out human rights abuses. By publicizing these, Amnesty hopes to stop them.

In many parts of China, as well as in Tibet, not everyone can enjoy the list of rights laid down by the United Nations. In China, people are allowed by law to have freedom of speech, freedom of religion, freedom to disagree with the government and many other freedoms. In practice these rights can be severely limited. Amnesty International, for example, knows that many people in China, and also in Tibet, have been sent to prison for a long time only because they criticized the government in

a public place, or even in private amongst a group of their friends. In China, unlike in most Western countries, a prisoner is believed to be guilty until he or she is proved innocent – and less than two per cent of court cases are won by those who are accused of a crime. So once you have been accused, you are unlikely to escape punishment. This might mean anything from a fine to imprisonment, or even death.

Accusations of genocide

As many as 1.5 million Tibetans may have died as a direct result of the Chinese invasion of Tibet. This is such an enormous figure that some have said that the Chinese authorities are guilty of genocide towards the

Tibetans. Genocide means trying to kill a whole nation, or an entire race or a complete group of people who practise the same religion. Certainly, in 1959 and 1960, the International Commission of Jurists (a highly respected body of lawyers and judges) said genocide was being committed by the Chinese upon the Tibetan nation. The Chinese estimate that 87,000 Tibetans died as a result of the 1959 National Uprising, while Tibetan exiles put the figure much higher and say 430,000 died in the Uprising and during the following 15 years.

Imprisonment without trial

While it is difficult to be sure of the exact figures, it is known that thousands who opposed the People's Republic of China at

➡ In Lhasa, the activities of the Tibetans are watched very closely at all times by Chinese troops and secret police.

this time were imprisoned without trial, or after unfair trials, in special camps. Conditions in these were so bad, and the prisoners were so ill treated, that thousands died in the camps. Those who did not die were not released until the 1970s.

Jigme Sangpo

Takna Jigme Sangpo was one of these prisoners. He was a primary school teacher in Lhasa in 1960 when he was first arrested for 'corrupting the minds of children with reactionary ideas'. This probably means wishing the old social structure could be restored. He was imprisoned for 19 years until 1979 and then had to work under close observation for a further four before being sent back to prison. On 6 December 1991,

he was put into solitary confinement because he and three of his fellow prisoners apparently shouted slogans in support of Tibetan independence. Amnesty International adopted him as one of its 'prisoners of conscience' and grew very concerned about the state of his health and the conditions of his detention. For ten years it repeatedly asked government authorities for more information about him, but never received any replies. He was eventually released in December 2002. He was Tibet's longest-serving political prisoner.

Demonstrations

After 1979, some things became a little easier for most people in Tibet. For example, a small number of monasteries which had been closed or partially destroyed were reopened and restored. Tourists were allowed into some parts of the country for the first time to increase China's stocks of foreign money. Taxes were reduced and peasants were given more freedom in the crops they were allowed to grow. However, monks and

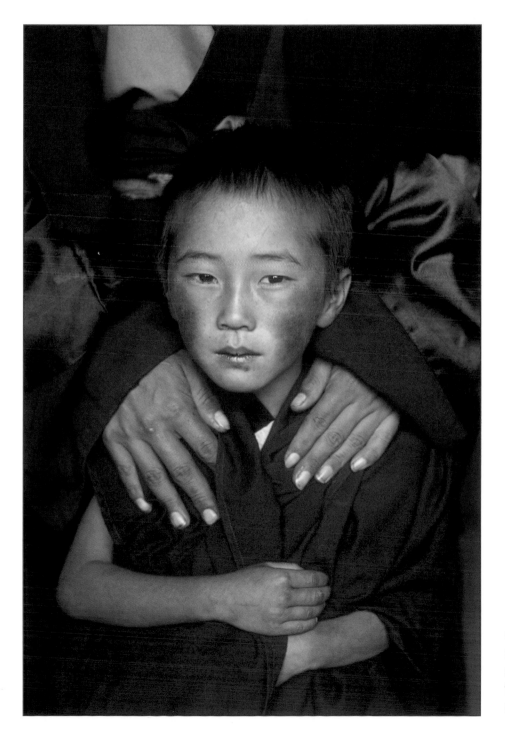

← A young Tibetan monk. Some monasteries were reopened after the 1979 uprisings, but they remain the focus for demonstrations in Tibet.

↑ One of the many Tibetans shot during the demonstrations against the Chinese occupation of Tibet. Peaceful demonstrations continue to be met with violence in Tibet.

nuns continued to be arrested for speaking out against the Chinese or otherwise acting in a way that the government did not like. (Monks and nuns in Tibet are often the people who lead demonstrations because they do not marry and therefore have no husband, wife or children who might be imprisoned and tortured if they are arrested.)

Since the late 1980s, there have been many demonstrations in the country. In March 1988 and March 1989 especially, thousands of Tibetans gathered near the Barkhor in the main square of Lhasa to protest against occupation. Chinese troops shot at them, even though the Tibetans had nothing more than stones or iron bars with

which to defend themselves. Amnesty International said: 'At least 60 civilians were reportedly killed and hundreds were injured by police and military forces' during the March 1989 demonstrations.

Continued problems

Twenty years later, people in Tibet are still demonstrating against the Chinese occupation of their country. In 2008, a series of demonstrations was held, and the Chinese increased the military and police presence, particularly in Lhasa. The monasteries are still the focal points of the demonstrations, and some monks have died from hunger or even killed themselves to bring their protest to the attention of the world.

The Chinese government was accused by Tibetans – and other countries around the world – of using unnecessary force to put down these demonstrations. Other countries are starting to understand how the Tibetans are suffering and are making their support of Tibet known. The Chinese government still says it is trying to find a peaceful way of resolving the problems in Tibet and even accused the Dalai Lama of encouraging a violent protest. Throughout all the years of his exile, though, the Dalai Lama has believed in peaceful protests against Chinese occupation of his country. Some young Tibetans have grown discouraged by this, because they feel that it has not achieved anything. They think that more direct, and violent, action is required to free Tibet.

Political prisoners

Enormous numbers of arrests are still being made. There are many reports that political prisoners suffer extreme ill treatment at the hands of the authorities. Once they have been arrested, prisoners can be severely beaten or punished in different ways. Most people treated in this way are demonstrators. Often, the only crime these prisoners have committed is to press for Tibet's independence – usually in a peaceful way.

⊙ Drapchi prison (front, right), the most notorious prison in Lhasa. It is thought that about 100 political prisoners are being held here.

6 Environmental destruction

Some people feel that China's plunder of Tibet's natural resources has been thoughtless and uncontrolled. For a long time, Chinese people have called Tibet the Western Treasure House, and one of the reasons why the country was invaded in the first place was to allow China access to Tibet's wealth of trees, minerals and animals. During the last 60 years, the chopping down of acres of forest, the rise in the human population and the marked increase in hunting have changed the balance of nature quite dramatically. In the old days, Tibet's wildlife was well protected, partly because Buddhists believe you should not kill another creature unless strictly necessary. In any case, the population was so low compared with the size of the country that wild animals and birds thrived. It is said that large herds of wild yak and antelope, as well as musk deer and wild ass roamed in certain areas. It was even possible to see rare snow leopards, lynx, Himalayan brown bears and monkeys. Of the bird life, there were eagles, white pheasants, Brahmini ducks, cranes and many other species.

⊕ Cows in the fertile Lhasa valley. Tibetan farmers have protested that the new chemical fertilizers they are forced to buy pollute the water and soil, and poison their animals.

⊕ These wild ass are just one example of Tibet's rich wildlife. Much of the wildlife is under threat because the Chinese government is not helping to preserve it.

Wildlife decline

The Chinese people, on the whole, have a different attitude towards wildlife than the Tibetans. The Chinese do not rely on it for their livelihoods. In the past, Chinese soldiers are known to have machine-gunned entire herds of wild ass for food or even just for fun. Chinese settlers have hunted the snow leopard, Himalayan monkeys and wild yak to the edge of extinction.

All over China and Tibet in the late 1950s, there was a Campaign Against the Four Pests: birds, flies, rats and mosquitoes. Everybody was told they had to kill a number of these creatures every week. Schoolboys were issued with catapults while schoolgirls were given fly-swats for the job. The result was that thousands of birds were killed and some species never recovered: doves, pigeons and some kinds of geese and ducks, for example, are no longer seen in Tibet.

Sky burial

Christians and Muslims burn or bury their dead, but in Tibet, wood is scarce and the ground is extremely dry for much of the year. Traditionally, therefore, Tibetans cut the dead body into pieces, mix it with meal and lay the remains out on a special rock for the eagles to peck clean.

Nuclear development

The Tibetan plateau is also rich in minerals. Uranium, used to make nuclear weapons,

Timber trucks loading logs beside a deforested slope in Tibet. Before the Chinese invasion, Tibet's ancient forests covered 221,800 square kilometres. Less than half of this is now still standing.

is found under the ground in the hills near Lhasa. These deposits of uranium are said to be the largest in the world. Gold, copper, zinc and minerals are also there in large amounts. The Chinese authorities, however, wasted no time in setting up mines to extract as many of these natural substances as possible, and in sending them back to China for use there.

The Tibetans have a reputation as a peace-loving people. They do not want another country's nuclear weapons on their soil but it is said that the Chinese army has placed a large part of its nuclear arsenal on the Tibetan plateau. This is because it is so high above sea level that the rockets will be able to travel further if they are launched. In the 1960s, China built one of its largest nuclear missile sites at Nagchuka, only 320 kilometres north of Lhasa. This top secret place is believed to contain about 90 nuclear missiles but nobody outside China knows for sure since it is heavily guarded by soldiers. In 1995, however, the Chinese did admit that there was a high-level nuclear waste dump on the Tibetan plateau.

Nuclear development

For centuries, Tibetans cut down trees whenever they needed timber, but they replanted them. The population was small and they cut down only what was necessary for their own purposes. China is an immensely populated country and its invasion of Tibet meant that suddenly it had access to a huge new source of wood that its own population could use. The Chinese built roads for easy access and then started laying waste great expanses of forest. Many hillsides that had once been leafy and green were suddenly bare. What made things worse was that often the lumberjacks took away only the best logs, and left the rest to rot on the ground.

Over the years, lorries have carried load after load of logs away to China. Sometimes 50 trucks an hour have been seen leaving Tibet. Timber has also been floated down the rivers to make transportation easier. So many logs have been carried away by this method that one tourist reported travelling beside a river that was choked with logs for 300 km.

Only a quarter of the trees that are being cut down in China are being replanted. As a result, the Chinese government has now passed laws forbidding such wholesale destruction of forests and encouraging the 'vigorous' replanting of trees. However, Tibet is thousands of kilometres away from Beijing, the capital of China, where these laws are being made. Inside the country, local leaders

⬇ Lorries carrying timber out of Tibet. Logging is an important source of jobs in Tibet.

◔ A flooded village in Bangladesh. Because so many trees have now been cut down in Tibet, water that would have been soaked up by trees runs far downhill and causes flooding.

are not making sure that the policies of the central authorities are being properly enforced. This means that large numbers of trucks, piled high with logs, are still leaving every day for China.

Trees help keep the balance of nature. If large numbers are cut down, this can seriously damage not only the landscape near the trees but also places much farther away. Trees help the earth soak up rainfall and they keep the soil on a hill in place. If the trees are cut down, there is nothing to stop heavy rain from rushing down the bare hillside and taking the top layer of soil with it. This mixture of water and earth comes to

rest a long way away in the bottom of the rivers and then causes floods. Back on the hillside, though, it is not so easy to grow things without that top layer of soil.

Forests absorb heat from the sun. Now that so many have been cut down in Tibet, it takes longer for the earth of the Tibetan plateau to warm up. This in turn affects India, Bangladesh and some other South-east Asian countries, and means the rains there begin later than they should and are not so heavy. By allowing so many trees to be cut down in Tibet, Chinese officials are harming not only Tibet itself but the abilities of these other countries to grow their crops.

7 Resistance

It is very difficult for Tibetans inside the country to protest against Chinese occupation and very dangerous for them to do so. Some very brave men and women achieve what they can by demonstrating in the streets and trying to oppose the Chinese authorities whenever possible. Some courageous people try to send messages to the outside world. For example, even at the height of martial law, tourists were being slipped pieces of paper that said:

'We appeal to all those who uphold human dignity to help Tibet to regain its independence. In the meantime, help to send United Nations, Amnesty International, Asia Watch and Minority Rights Group fact-finding missions throughout Tibet – including setting up a UN office in Tibet.'

Leader in exile

The person who has done most to help the Tibetans is the Dalai Lama himself.

⬆ Tibetan refugee children in India demonstrating against the occupation of their country by the Chinese.

The Dalai Lama showing the Nobel Peace Prize he won in 1989.

Although he no longer lives inside the country, he is still worshipped by many as their god-king and is respected by Tibetans across the world as their political leader. After he fled from Tibet in 1959, the Indian government allowed him and many of those who followed him to settle in Dharamsala. This is a small cluster of villages 2,000 metres up in the hills of northern India, to which Tibetan refugees can come and receive support and hope, and where some of them can live.

Refugees

Refugees continue to leave Tibet at the rate of about four people a day. At first they are most

The Panchen Lama

The Panchen Lama is second in importance only to the Dalai Lama. There is disagreement about who the current Panchen Lama is. The Chinese say it is Qoigyijabu, but the Tibetans recognize Gedhun Choekyi Nyima as the eleventh Panchen Lama. Gedhun Choekyi Nyima was born in 1995, and was named Panchen Lama a month after his birth. However, the Chinese government immediately removed him from Tibet and no one knows exactly where he is. The Tibetan government in exile claims he is being held prisoner by the Chinese – the youngest political prisoner in the world.

commonly welcomed and looked after in Nepal and northern India, but after that they may live in Tibetan settlements that have been established in southern India. Some also move to other parts of the world.

Tibetan culture outside Tibet

Since much of the culture, Buddhism and medical practice of Tibet have been destroyed inside the country, refugees are doing their best to make them flourish outside. They have built a large library in Dharamsala as well as several monasteries, a centre for Tibetan medicine, and a place where Tibetan handicrafts are being made. There is also an institute of performing arts where opera, folk songs, poetry and other traditional arts are taught.

← Tibetan dancers in Dharamsala, India, where members of the Tibetan Institute of Performing Arts work to preserve Tibetan culture.

Great efforts are being made to keep the special traditions and teachings of Tibetan Buddhism alive. This is not easy because so much religious literature has been destroyed and so many of the greatest teachers have been killed inside Tibet. However, in many parts of the world, Tibetan Buddhism is becoming a popular subject to study. Increasing numbers of people are now practising the religion and some – not just Tibetans – are training to become monks and nuns. Today, there are Tibetan Buddhist centres in most Western countries where you can learn more about this ancient religion.

Support in the media

Those who are not Tibetan but who are concerned about the situation in the country, use the power of publicity on the radio and television, and in the newspapers to make sure people do not forget about Tibet. Support groups exist in many countries to make sure that correct information is always available to journalists and others who need it to make well-informed statements about the effect of the Chinese presence in Tibet.

Over the last few years, some writers and documentary film makers have entered Tibet secretly in order to find out for themselves

⬆ A Tibetan building. Elaborate wood carving and the use of bright colours are features of traditional Tibetan architecture.

⬆ The Dalai Lama welcoming Indian visitors to Dharamsala. The Tibetan leader believes it is important to spread word of his people's hardship throughout the world.

what is really happening and to make their investigations known. In the 1980s, during some of the worst times in Tibet, a female journalist disguised herself as a Tibetan peasant and travelled all over the country, secretly making a film. This was the first film to come out of Tibet in over 40 years. Even today it is difficult for foreign media to get into the country, so it is often hard to know just what the situation is.

Olympic troubles

The Chinese government relaxed the laws on foreign journalists being allowed into the country during the Olympic Games in 2008.

China hosted the games, although there was a great deal of controversy about this. Many countries felt that China should not be the hosts because of their actions in Tibet. During the violent suppression of the demonstrations in Tibet in early 2008, some countries even threatened to boycott the Olympic Games that were due to start later in the year.

Dealing with the Chinese

The Dalai Lama and his advisers have tried several times to negotiate with the Chinese authorities for peace but have had little success. In 1988, for example, he put forward

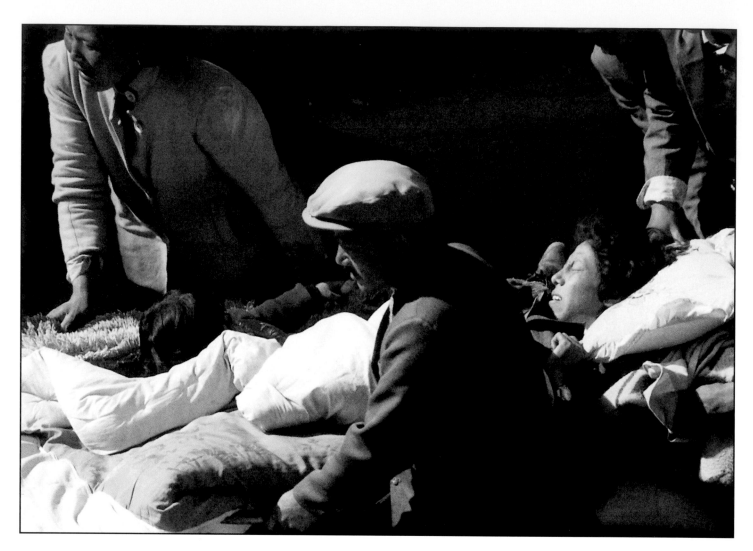

⬆ A demonstrator shot during the March 1989 protest in Lhasa. Scenes like this have become increasingly common during the last few years in Tibet.

the Strasbourg Proposal, in which he suggested they could keep control of foreign and defence affairs in the country so long as they allowed Tibetans to run everything else. He calls this his 'middle way'. The Chinese government still rejects the proposal because they do not believe the Dalai Lama is really willing to give up independence. The Chinese think the 'middle way' is just a stepping stone for the Dalai Lama to regain independence for Tibet.

Non-violent resistance

The Dalai Lama has always believed that resistance to the Chinese should be made in

a non-violent way and that, in the end, this approach will be successful. In December 1989, he was awarded the Nobel Peace Prize, showing that other people agree with his views. Some of the more important world leaders have recently met him to at least talk about the situation in Tibet. Before he won the prize, many of them refused to see him in case they offended China.

In March 1992, members of the United Nations Human Rights Commission were expected to vote to condemn China's behaviour in Tibet. In the end, they did not do so: the Western nations did not want to spoil their opportunities for trading with

China, and the world's poorer countries did not want China to stop giving them aid.

It is still difficult for many countries to openly support Tibet. China is a large and increasingly influential country. However, more foreign governments are starting to take notice of what is happening in Tibet and to express their support for the Tibetans. In addition, there are support groups in countries all over the world that publicize the events in Tibet and bring them to the world's attention.

Violent resistance

Some groups in Tibet, in particular the Lion Tiger Youth Association, believed that the time for peaceful demonstrations was over. They thought that if the Chinese treated them with violence, the only way to respond was with violence. They said that the Dalai Lama's method has not worked and it was time for a new strategy. On the whole, however, most Tibetans still hope and believe that the strategy of non-violent resistance is the best course of action.

⬆ The Lion Tiger Youth Association was a group that suggested that non-violent demonstrations had failed: independence might only be achieved through violent protests.

8 The future

As we have seen, children like Pema Norbu in the Changtang and Paljor Sonam in Lhasa are growing up in a very different Tibet from the country their grandparents grew up in. When those children were born, the Chinese had already been ruling Tibet for several decades and had forced immense changes on its people and their culture. The terrible cost in terms of human life and freedom is one aspect of Chinese occupation, and is continuing to this day: Tibetans are still being imprisoned and tortured for protesting against the Chinese authorities. Other aspects are the destruction of the monastic way of life,

◑ An old woman and young children in the street in Lhasa. The Tibet these children are growing up in is a very different country from the one the old woman remembers, and even the children's Tibet may not exist for much longer.

⬆ Monks debating at Tashilumpo Monastery, one of the few monasteries in Tibet that still work.

the high unemployment amongst Tibetans and the ruin of the environment.

The beacon of freedom

Imagine what it would be like to have another country's soldiers and police standing on the street corners of your town, watching what you are doing. If you put up a poster telling them to go home, wave your country's flag or follow a demonstration they can arrest you or members of your family – and there is absolutely nothing you can do about it. You see your country's trees being cut down and trucked across the border, you are even having to learn your lessons in the invader's language and not your own – and there is nothing you can do about that either.

The situation inside Tibet does not look especially hopeful, but the Dalai Lama believes that things may be changing for the better in several small ways. For example,

some governments are now paying more attention to protecting human rights and the environment than they have ever done before. This may mean they make more of an effort to help the Tibetans in their struggle for survival. However, unless the world's leaders put pressure on the Chinese government to change their policies, it is unlikely that life for the Tibetans will ease in the near future. The killings, torture and destruction of the Tibetan way of life have to be stopped soon, because as the Dalai Lama has said: 'This is the worst period in our 2,000-year long history. At this time, now, there is every danger that the entire Tibetan nation, with its own unique cultural heritage, will completely disappear… at a time when the beacon of freedom and democracy is burning brighter in many parts of the world, what the Tibetan people need is the protection of international concern and support.'

Glossary

Activists People who take action to achieve a particular aim.

Ass An animal related to the horse, but having longer ears.

Barkhor The street encircling the Jokhang, which is also used as a pilgrim circuit. Pilgrims prostrate around the circuit, wearing special knee and elbow pads to protect themselves.

Beijing The capital of China.

Dalai Lama The spiritual and political leader of Tibet. Today's Dalai Lama is the fourteenth in succession: he does not live in Tibet, since he fled from the Chinese. He now lives in Dharamsala in northern India.

Himalayas The highest mountain range in the world, in which all the world's mountains over 8,000 metres are found.

Illiterate Unable to read and write.

Lhasa The ancient capital of Tibet.

Linkhor A pilgrim route that encircled Lhasa. It has now been ruined by having roads and buildings built over it by the Chinese authorities.

Monastery A place in which members of a religious group live together to study and worship. Traditionally, monasteries are places of great learning. In Tibet, at least until the Chinese invasion, the monasteries were a central part of life for almost everyone. During the Cultural Revolution (see page 19) most of the monasteries were wrecked: by 1978 all but 13 of almost six thousand monasteries in Tibet had been ruined.

Mule An animal that is the result of crossing a donkey with a horse.

Nobel Peace Prize A highly respected prize given for outstanding contributions to peace by a committee of the Norwegian parliament. The Dalai Lama was awarded the Nobel Peace Prize in 1989 in recognition of his campaign for peaceful resistance to the Chinese invasion.

Panchen Lama The most senior person in Tibet after the Dalai Lama. The most recent Panchen Lama was ousted by the Chinese and is believed to be living in China under guard of the government there.

Peasants People who work either in small-scale agriculture or in their own homes. They do not usually earn very much, and often struggle to find enough to eat.

Plateau A wide, generally level, area of land that is high up.

Potala The winter home in Tibet of the Dalai Lama. The Potala stands in the middle of Lhasa and is built on a hill, so it dominates the skyline of the town.

Prostration Lying face downwards as a way of showing humility and respect.

Revolt A rebellion or uprising against authority.

T.A.R. Tibetan Autonomous Region. One part of the original three provinces of old Tibet. This part of the old country of Tibet is all that the Chinese government now recognizes as Tibetan. This means that the Dalai Lama and other campaigners cannot discuss the fate of large parts of their country with the Chinese.

Torture Causing extreme physical pain to someone in order to extract information from them or to break their resistance.

Tsampa Barley ground to the consistency of flour, which was traditionally the staple food of most Tibetans.

Vision A vivid mental picture, which often occurs in a dream, that is thought to foretell the future.

Yak A species of cattle with long horns and shaggy hair that is found only in the Himalayan region. Yaks have traditionally been used in the Tibetan area as beasts of burden, to carry goods and people.

Further reading

The Dalai Lama: Peacemaker from Tibet, Chris Gibb (Wayland, 2003)

Tibet (Cultures of the World), Patricia M. Levy (Benchmark Books, 2007)

Tibet (Enchantment of the World), Patricia K. Kummer (Children's Press, 2003)

The Story of Tibet: Conversations with the Dalai Lama, Thomas Laird (Grove Press, 2007)

Folk Tales from Eastern Tibet (Library of Tibetan Works and Archives, 2006)

Further information

Minority Rights Group International's Education Project produces learning material and information for teachers covering many aspects of minority rights. www.minorityrights.org/

Amnesty International
www.amnesty.org

International Tibet Support Group
www.tibet.org/

Tibet House
625 Broadway,
12th Floor,
New York, NY 10012, USA
www.tibethouse.org

Australia Tibet Council
www.atc.org.au

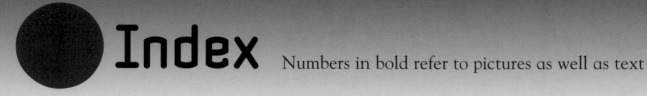

Index

Numbers in bold refer to pictures as well as text